Munin

No. 72

# The FIRST BOOK of

EDMUND WARD (PUBLISHERS) LTD.

LONDON

# norse

# legends

*Written and with pictures by*

## KATHLEEN ELGIN

FOR KATHY

First published in Great Britain by
EDMUND WARD (PUBLISHERS) LIMITED
194-200, Bishopsgate, London, E.C.2
1965

Original edition published in the United States of America by
FRANKLIN WATTS, INC.
575 Lexington Avenue, New York 22
1956

Copyright © 1956 by Franklin Watts, Inc.

Printed Offset in Great Britain by
STRAKER BROTHERS LTD
Bishopsgate, London, E.C.2

# CONTENTS

## SOME GODS AND GODDESSES OF THE NORTH

**AIGIR,** god of the sea

**BALDUR,** god of light and spring

**BURE,** father of the gods

**FREY,** god of rain, sunshine and the fruits of the earth

**FREYA,** goddess of love and beauty

**FRIGGA,** goddess of earth, marriage and motherly love

**HEIMDALL,** watchman of the Rainbow Bridge

**HELA,** goddess of the dead

**HODUR,** god of darkness

**HOENIR,** similar to Odin in some myths, god of hope

**IDUN,** goddess of youth

**LOKI,** god of fire

**MANI,** god of the moon

**MIMIR,** guardian of the Well of Wisdom

**NIORD,** god of the wind

**ODIN,** king of the gods, god of war and wisdom

**SOL,** goddess of the sun

**THIALFI,** servant of Odin

**THOR,** god of thunder

**TYR,** god of truth and battle

# HOW TO PRONOUNCE THE NAMES

| | | | | |
|---|---|---|---|---|
| AEGIR | .. | .. A-gir | HYMIR .. | .. HEE-mir |
| AESIR | .. | .. A-sir | IARNGRIEPER | .. YERN-gri-per |
| ASGARD | .. | .. As-gard | IDUN .. | .. ee-DOON |
| ASKEE | .. | .. As-kee | JOTUNHEIM .. | .. jer-TOON-hime |
| AUDHUMLA | .. | .. ou-DOOM-la | LOGI .. | .. Lo-gee |
| AUSTRI | .. | .. Ous- tri | LOKI .. | .. Lo-kee |
| BALDUR | .. | .. BAL-door | MANI .. | .. MAH-nee |
| BERGELMIR | .. | .. ber-GEL-mir | MEGINGIORD | .. MAY-gin-gyerd |
| BIFROST | .. | .. BEE-frost | MIDGARD .. | .. MID-gard |
| BURE | .. | .. BUR-ee | MIMIR .. | .. MEE-mir |
| DAIN | .. | .. DA-in | MIOLNIR .. | .. MYEL-nir |
| DRAUPNIR | .. | .. DROUP-nir | MUNIN .. | .. MOON-in |
| DUNEYR | .. | .. Doo-nire | NANNA .. | .. NAHN-na |
| DURATHOR | .. | .. Doo-ra-thor | NIORD .. | .. NYERD |
| DVALIN | .. | .. DVA-lin | NORDRI .. | .. NOR-dri |
| ELLI | .. | .. EL-lee | ODIN .. | .. O-din |
| EMBLA | .. | .. EM-bla | SAEHRIMNIR | .. SA-rim-nir |
| FENSALIR | .. | .. FEN-sa-lir | SKOLL .. | .. SKELL |
| FREY | .. | .. FRI | SKRYMIR .. | .. SKREE-mir |
| FREYA | .. | .. FRI-a | SLEIPNIR .. | .. SLIPE-nir |
| FRIGGA | .. | .. FRIG-a | SOL .. .. | .. SOLE |
| FRIKI | .. | .. FRICK-ee | SUDRI .. | .. Soo-dri |
| GERI | .. | .. GER-ee | SURTR .. | .. Soor-truh |
| GLADSHEIM | .. | .. GLADZ-hime | THIALFI .. | .. the-ALF-ee |
| GULLINTANI | .. | .. GUL-in-tah-nee | THOR .. | .. THORE |
| GUNGNIR | .. | .. GUNG-nir | TYR .. | .. TEER |
| GYROLL | .. | .. GEE-roll | URDAR .. | .. OORD-ar |
| HATI | .. | .. HAH-tee | UTGARD-LOKI | .. OOT-gard-Lo-kee |
| HEIDRUN | .. | .. HI-droon | VALASKIALF | .. VAA-las-kyalf |
| HEIMDALL | .. | .. HIME-dal | VALHALLA .. | .. val-HAL-la |
| HELA | .. | .. HEL-a | VALKYRS .. | .. VAL-keers |
| HERMOD | .. | .. HER-mod | WESTRI .. | .. WES-tri |
| HODUR | .. | .. Ho-door | YGGDRASIL .. | .. IGG-dra-sil |
| HOENIR | .. | .. HER-nir | YMIR .. | .. EE-mir |
| HUGIN | .. | .. HOOG-in | | |

FINLAN

SWEDEN

NORWAY

OSLO °

STOCKHOLM °

NORTH SEA

DENMARK

COPENHAGEN

BALTIC SEA

GERMANY

*Lands of the Norse Legends*

# WHAT LEGENDS ARE

Legends are stories that have come down to us from long ago—stories that try to explain the world and how it began. Because there were once no scientists to tell people the reasons for things, men had to make up their own reasons. They invented gods and goddesses, giants and monsters, and said that they were responsible for the world and what happened to it.

The old legends tell us a great deal about the people who made them and the countries from which they came. The legends of Greece and Rome are bright and sunny in character, for these are sunny lands. But Norway, Denmark and Sweden, from which came the Norse legends, are rugged and harsh. The people of the North, of Norseland, led hard lives. The bitter cold, the lack of sunshine, the stormy seas and the icebergs were their enemies. So the Norse legends are harsh and rugged. They describe the struggle of the good forces against the bad forces of nature—warmth against cold, light against darkness. The Norse gods and goddesses, giants and monsters, are huge, like the mountains and the icebergs.

Many of the old Norse legends have been forgotten over the years, but there are enough of them left to give us a good idea of what people once thought and believed in their cold northern home.

11

THE GIANT WITH THE FLAMING SWORD

# THE BEGINNING

In the beginning the world was mist swirling over a vast field of jagged and cavernous ice. Later, great fires began to burn under the ice. They were guarded by the flame giant, Surtr.

Surtr carried a flaming sword that sent forth showers of sparks. The sparks fell hissing on to the blocks of ice and partly melted them away.

As the ice melted, it took the form of the frost giant Ymir and his cow, Audhumla, the nourisher of life. In time, other giants grew out of the ice and mist.

One day, while Ymir's cow was feeding on the salt and frost from the ice, a huge head appeared through the frozen mass. In three days the rest of the figure appeared. It was Bure, the first god.

When Bure saw the huge, terrifying shapes of the frost giants, he knew at once that they were evil and would be the enemies of the gods. His powerful voice rang out through the icy caverns, calling his unborn sons. By his magic they appeared and he told them of the everlasting battle they must wage with the frost giants, to keep them from overpowering the world.

In the mists of the beginning the gods and giants battled for the world. The gods won, but Bure was killed. All the giants were destroyed except Bergelmir and his wife. They fled to the outer edges of the world and made for themselves a land called Jotunheim, near the North Pole.

From Bergelmir and his wife were descended a whole new race of frost and mountain giants.

## Sky and earth

After Bure's death, his grandson Odin became king of the gods. He and his brothers Hoenir and Loki made the earth from the frost giant Ymir's body and called it Midgard, or Middle Garden. They placed Midgard in the middle of the world, directly beneath the cloudland kingdom of Asgard, home of the gods.

From Ymir's skull they made the vaulted sky and commanded four strong dwarfs to hold it up. The dwarfs were Nordri, Sudri, Austri and Westri: North, South, East and West.

From Ymir's blood the gods made the sea around the earth, thus separating the earth from the giants' land of ice and fire on the outer edges of the world.

Then the gods made a wall round Midgard out of Ymir's eyebrows. Of his bones they made the mountains and of his hair the trees. They flung his brains into the sky to make the clouds, and Odin took sparks from the land of ice and fire to make the sun and moon and stars. The sun made plants grow and the earth became beautiful. Then Odin divided time into day and night.

NEWLY CREATED EARTH

When earth and sky were finished, the gods took the ash tree, Aske, and the elder tree, Embla, and changed them into a man and a woman. Odin gave Aske and Embla souls, Hoenir gave them senses and movement, and Loki sent the blood running through their veins and filled them with emotions.

The gods gave Midgard to Aske and Embla for their home. The children and grandchildren of this newly created man and woman were the Vikings who roved the seas, often as pirates, and the goldenbearded warriors of Norseland. The gods always watched over and helped them, for they had made them in their own image.

## The tree of life

Now Odin made the gigantic ash tree, the tree of life called Yggdrasil, which filled the whole world. It had three tremendous roots. One was in the land of ice and fire. One was in Midgard near the Sea, or Well, of Wisdom, guarded by the wise old god Mimir. And one root was in Asgard near the Urdar Fountain, where the gods gathered daily for their council.

The tree Yggdrasil was always green. Its topmost branches shaded Odin's palace in Asgard. It offered food for Odin's goat, Heidrun, which gave an everlasting supply of wine for the gods' feasts. Four deer also grazed on the tree. Their names were Dain, Dvalin, Duneyr and Durathor. From the

16

horns of the deer dripped honey to fill the rivers of the world.

The tree was cared for by three sisters known as the Norns, or Fates. They represented the past, the present and the future. Every day they sprinkled the tree with holy water from the Urdar Fountain. As the water trickled down through the leaves, it gave honey to the bees.

The Norns also guarded the golden apples that grew on the tree. These apples had the power to renew the youth of anyone who ate them. The Norns allowed only Idun, goddess of youth, to pick the golden fruit. Every day Idun filled her basket with it and gave it to the gods so that they might renew their youth.

## Heaven

The entrance to Asgard, kingdom of the gods, was over the Rainbow Bridge, Bifrost, which was built of fire, water and air. The bridge rose from the outer edges of the land of ice and fire and arched high over Midgard. Because the gods feared that the giants would use the bridge to invade Asgard, they set Heimdall, son of Odin, to guard it. They gave him a strong and mighty sword with which to fight off all the giants and a loud trumpet with which to warn the gods of approaching danger.

In Asgard the gods lived in gold and silver palaces created for them by Odin. Three of the palaces belonged to Odin himself. One was Gladsheim, and in it stood twelve golden thrones. These thrones were for the twelve gods who ruled heaven and earth and who were known as the Aesir, or supporters of the world.

The second of Odin's palaces was Valaskialf, where his throne stood. And the third was Valhalla, where he entertained the earthly heroes who had fallen in battle.

Valhalla had five hundred and forty doors, each wide enough for eight hundred warriors to march through it abreast. Above the main gate were a boar's head and an eagle. The eagle's sharp eyes could see even to the outer edges of the world.

The walls of Valhalla were made of shining spears and its roof was of golden shields. Inside were long banqueting tables, lined with benches that were decorated with precious armour.

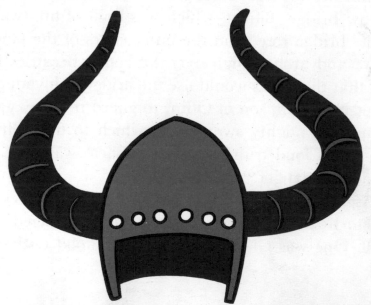

NORSE WARRIOR

# THE GODS

Odin was not only king of the gods, but god of wisdom and of war as well. In size he was tremendous. He had a long, silvery beard and wore a hooded cloak that looked like the sky dappled with fleecy clouds. His golden helmet was shaped like an eagle. Although there was great feasting in Asgard, Odin lived on wine alone. He gave his share of food to the two wolves, Geri and Friki, that were his hunting hounds and always crouched at his feet.

Odin had two ravens, Hugin and Munin, Thought and Memory. Every day he sent Hugin and Munin forth to find out what was happening in the world, and report to him.

Odin's wife, Frigga, was goddess of the clouds, of marriage and of motherly love. She dressed in a white robe with a golden belt. From the belt hung her keys. That was the way Norse housewives dressed and she was their patron goddess.

From his throne Odin looked out over the whole world, but Frigga gazed mostly towards the south and west, towards those warm and sunny lands for which the Vikings sailed. Frigga usually stayed in her palace of Fensalir, which means hall of mists. There she sat at her wheel, spinning golden threads or great webs of clouds. If you look in the sky some starry night, you can see Frigga's spinning-wheel in the constellation which we call Orion.

20

ODIN

Frigga had four sons. Two of them were twins. The twins were Hodur the blind, god of darkness, and Baldur the beautiful, god of light, best loved of all the gods. Frigga's other sons were Hermod, messenger of the gods, and Tyr, god of battle.

Loki, god of fire, was Odin's brother. He was a great mischief-maker, but so clever that for a long time he deceived the other gods into thinking him a fine fellow.

One of Loki's children was the Midgard Serpent, whose tail reached round the world. When the seas were wild and stormy, the Norsemen believed that the Midgard Serpent was lashing its tail.

Another of Loki's children was Hela, goddess of the dead. She ruled the underworld of Hel. She was half pink and half blue and had a very frightening face.

Thor, son of Odin, was the god of thunder. The giants feared him more than any other god. He drove a chariot pulled by two red-eyed, shaggy goats, Toothcracker and Toothgnasher, whose flying hoofs showered sparks. The rumble of Thor's chariot across the sky was like thunder.

Thor's wife was Sif, the golden-haired. Sif's beautiful hair represented to the gods, and to the people on earth, the golden grain of the harvest fields.

Heimdall, watchman of the Rainbow Bridge, had golden teeth. He was often called Gullintani, the golden-toothed. His ears were so keen that he could hear the grass grow and

MIDGARD SERPENT

the wool growing on the backs of sheep. He could see more than a hundred miles by day or night, and he was so tireless that he needed less sleep than a bird.

Niord was god of the wind and the sea. His children were Frey, the god of sunshine, and Freya, goddess of beauty. Freya wore a golden necklace that represented the fruitfulness of the earth. She rode in a chariot drawn by white cats, her favourite animals. Sometimes she flew through the air in a gown made of falcon's feathers.

Sol, god of the sun, and Mani, god of the moon, drove their chariots daily across the sky. They were pursued by two wolves, Skoll and Hati, or Repulsion and Hatred. The wolves wanted to swallow the sun and moon and return the world to darkness. Sometimes they almost succeeded. Then there was an eclipse of the sun or the moon. When that happened, the people on earth raised such loud cries of terror and sorrow that the wolves, frightened, dropped their prey. But immediately they started the chase all over again.

In Valhalla lived Odin's battle-maidens, the Valkyrs. These beautiful young women had dazzling white arms and long, golden hair. They wore blood-red armour and golden helmets. On their swift white horses, they charged into the fiercest battles to lift the fallen warriors from the field or the dying Vikings from their sinking ships. The Valkyrs chose the bravest of the dead and dying and carried them in triumph over the shimmering Rainbow Bridge to Valhalla.

There the Valkyrs laid down their armour and dressed in beautiful white robes. On the long banqueting tables, they set before the heroes great feasts of meat from the magic boar Saehrimnir. Saehrimnir came to life again each day, after he had been cooked and eaten, so that there was an everlasting supply of meat for the tables of Valhalla. There was also an everlasting supply of wine from the goat Heidrun. The Valkyrs served it in golden cups, or in the whitened skulls of the heroes' enemies.

When the heroes had finished the feast, they were magically cured of their wounds. Then the Valkyrs carried them back to the battle.

The Norsemen worshipped the Valkyrs, for they believed that they gave nourishment to the earth and freshness to the pines and the northern air. They believed that the frost and dew dropped from the flowing manes of the Valkyrs' horses as they galloped across the sky. They saw the great white horses in the running clouds on a windy day. They saw the Valkyrs' golden spears in the forked lightning. And when the Northern Lights flared and crackled in the sky, they believed that the Valkyrs were riding.

From their palaces in Asgard the gods ruled heaven and earth. The people on earth, forever trying to understand why things happened this way or that way, made for themselves the stories of the gods' adventures which you will read in this book.

# HOW ODIN LOST ONE EYE

Odin had three great treasures. One of them was his eight-footed horse Sleipnir, which carried him through the clouds faster than the wind. Another was the magic ring Draupnir, which dropped eight new golden rings every nine nights. The last treasure was the spear Gungnir, which never failed to strike its target.

But Odin wanted a treasure greater than any of these. He wanted the greatest treasure of all—wisdom. So one day he journeyed to Midgard to drink from Mimir's well.

The old god Mimir knew how valuable this treasure of wisdom would be to the king of the gods. With it he would be able to see even into the future, which is veiled from ordinary men. Mimir decided to make Odin pay well for a drink from the Well of Wisdom.

'You may drink,' he said, 'if you will give me one of your eyes.'

Odin did not hesitate. He plucked out one eye and gave it to Mimir. Mimir dropped the eye into the well and it sank to the bottom. There it lay, shining pale and beautiful in the clear, dark water. It became the brightness of the moon, and Odin's remaining eye was the brightness of the sun.

Mimir dipped his drinking cup into the well and handed it to Odin. Odin raised the cup to his bearded lips and took a

ODIN

long drink of magic water. From that time on, he was wiser than any other god or mortal and he could see the future clear as day.

But there is a great sadness that goes with the power to look into the future. Now Odin could see ahead to the terrible things that would happen to the gods some day. That is why for most of the time, he would just sit on his great golden throne and think.

Sometimes Odin left his throne to go down to earth, to see how man was getting along. Then he pulled his helmet well down on his forehead to hide the secret of his missing eye.

# HOW THOR GOT HIS HAMMER BACK

Odin's son Thor was one of twelve gods who ruled heaven and earth. He was a gigantic god, with red hair and a great red beard. The gods had forbidden him to use the Rainbow Bridge because they were afraid that he would set it afire by the heat of his presence.

The red-bearded god had three weapons. The first was the magic belt called Megingiord, which doubled his strength when he wore it. The second was the mighty hammer Miolnir, the crusher, which returned to his hand after he had thrown it. This hammer was usually so fiery hot that Thor needed his third weapon, the iron glove named Iarngrieper, in order to hold it.

The giants feared Thor and his hammer more than anything in the world. At last, the king of the frost giants managed to steal the hammer and bury it miles deep under the ice of his country.

The theft of Thor's hammer caused great worry in Asgard. The gods knew that without his powerful weapon Thor could not protect them if the giants attacked. Thor thought that the clever Loki might be able to find away to get the hammer back, so he sent the mischief-maker to Jotunheim.

Loki came back with the news that the giants would return

Thor's hammer if the lovely Freya, goddess of beauty and love, would be the giant king's bride.

Freya was terrified at the thought of becoming the bride of a frost giant. Not even to save Asgard would she consent. So Loki persuaded Thor to disguise himself as Freya and he himself escorted the strange bride to the land of the giants.

The king of the frost giants received his veiled bride with joy. His servants prepared a banquet in her honour. For her alone they cooked the most tender portions of the meat and concocted sweets and other delicacies fit only for a goddess.

What was their surprise when the bride downed the meal with one gulp and finished it off with a full-grown ox, eight salmon and seven hundred and fifty-six gallons of wine!

Amazed, the frost giant asked Loki, 'Does she always eat like this?'

'No, no,' Loki hastened to assure him. 'It is only that she has not eaten for eight nights. She was so excited about meeting the great king of the giants that she could not touch a morsel.'

'That I can well understand,' said the bridegroom with satisfaction, for he was a conceited giant.

As the feast went on, he grew impatient to see his bride.

'Why must she veil her face from me?' he asked. 'Is she always so shy?'

'It is the shyness of humility,' said Loki quickly. 'Never has she been in the presence of so great a king.'

FROST GIANT

'That too I can understand,' said the conceited giant.

And with that he lifted one corner of her veil to take the tiniest peep at her face. He dropped the veil faster than he had lifted it and in a frightened voice asked Loki, 'Why do her eyes glisten with fire?'

'It is the fire of love you see,' said Loki.

The giant was satisfied with this explanation and ordered Thor's hammer to be brought to him, so that he might fulfil his part of the bargain he had made with the gods.

It took ten giant servants to carry Thor's hammer. The king lifted it in both hands and laid it on his bride's lap.

Immediately Thor seized the hammer, threw back his veil and shouted, 'It is not the beautiful Freya, but I, Thor!'

The red-bearded god threw the hammer with all his tremendous strength, killing the evil giant and all his followers.

# THOR'S JOURNEY TO THE GIANTS' LAND

From Jotunheim at the North Pole the giants sent icy winds and frost to nip the swelling flower-buds in Asgard. One day Thor decided to go to Jotunheim and put a stop to this mischief.

Thor travelled on foot and took with him for companions his servant Thialfi and the fire god Loki.

The first night of their journey, the three gods came to a great forest and there they looked for a place of rest. Loki discovered a large hall whose doorway stretched the whole length of the building. Since the hall appeared to be empty, Thor and his companions entered it and lay down to sleep. But no sooner had they closed their eyes than the hall began to shake violently. The three gods jumped up in alarm.

'An earthquake!' shouted Loki.

'Let us go into the small room on the right,' said Thor. 'It seems quieter there.'

The shaking ceased presently and Thor said. 'Go to sleep, my friends. I shall stand guard the rest of the night.'

At dawn Thor went outside and discovered a giant asleep near by. The giant stirred in his sleep and the ground trembled. So, thought the god, this is our earthquake! And he started to tiptoe away.

33

SLEEPING GIANT

Immediately the giant awoke, stretched himself lazily and said, 'My name is Skrymir, and I know by looking at your fiery-red beard that you must be Thor, god of thunder.'

Then the giant stood up, and looking down at Thor from his great height asked, 'Have you seen my other mitten by any chance? I seem to have only one.'

Thor looked about and saw that the large hall in which he and his companions had slept was actually the giant's mitten. The small room where they had gone for safety was the mitten's thumb.

He hid his surprise as he pointed out the mitten to the sleepy giant. Then, tightening his belt of strength, he said, 'Where are you travelling? Perhaps we can journey together.'

'I'm going to the capital of Jotunheim,' answered the giant.

'Good!' said Thor. 'Then let us travel together, for I am going to the same city.'

Before starting out, the giant put all of his own and the gods' provisions into his immense knapsack. He swung the knapsack over his shoulder and started in front to lead the way.

It was hard for the gods to keep up with the giant's huge steps. When finally they stopped for the night, they were tired and hungry. Skrymir lay down to sleep, but told the gods that they might dine on the food in his knapsack.

As the giant's snores once more began to shake the earth,

Thor tried to loosen the string which the giant had knotted around the knapsack. But try as he would, he could not loosen a single knot. Angry red sparks flew from his beard. In sudden rage he threw his hammer with all his strength at the giant's head.

Skrymir opened his eyes and asked drowsily, 'Did a leaf fall on my head? Aren't you finished with your dinner and ready for sleep?'

Thor was so astonished that he forgot his hunger and lay down to sleep. But sleep was impossible. The giant's snores echoed for miles and the ground shook like a broken ship.

Once more the thunder god reached for his hammer. He crept towards Skrymir and aimed a blow that should have broken the giant's skull.

The giant opened one eye. 'Has some moss from the tree fallen on my head?' he asked. 'Has the same thing happened to you?'

'I just awoke,' said Thor. 'I will try to go back to sleep.'

But Thor did not go back to sleep. He sat under a tree, planning the third blow he would give the giant. That one would be another matter!

A little before dawn the giant began to snore again. Thor grasped his hammer, raised it high and brought it down on the giant's skull with all his mighty strength.

But the giant sat up and said to the amazed god, 'This time an acorn must have fallen! Well, Thor, it is now almost daylight and we must be on our way. I have to go north before going to the city, so here we part company.'

As the giant strode away over the hills, his knapsack bouncing on his great shoulders, Loki shouted after him:

'No dinner and now no breakfast! Ill luck to you, heartless giant!'

'Let us all go on to meet the king of these giants,' said Thor. And the three gods set out along the dusty road to the capital.

They came at last to Jotunheim, a city so tall that even when they leaned backwards they could not see the tops of the towers. They entered the city and came to a palace built of huge blocks of ice, with tremendous icicles for pillars.

In the hall of the palace were the tallest giants the gods had ever seen. These giants brought Thor and his two companions to the king, Utgard-Loki, who looked down at them in amusement.

'You must be Thor, god of thunder,' said the giant king. 'What a small man you are! But perhaps you are stronger than you look. What mighty deeds can you and your companions do? Anyone who stays here must be able to do something better than anyone else.'

Loki was ravenously hungry after the long journey. He stepped forward and said, 'I can eat faster than anyone here!'

'You will amaze me if you can do that,' said Utgard-Loki, and he called for a tremendous giant whose name was Logi.

At a signal from the king, four servants then brought a long

LOKI

trough filled with meat. Loki and Logi faced each other at either end. At the king's word, they began to eat. Each ate like lightning. In a matter of minutes they met in the middle of the trough. Loki grinned in triumph. It looked like a tie, but to his amazement, while he had eaten the flesh in the trough, the giant had eaten through flesh and bone, and his end of the trough as well!

The king of the giants said to Thor, 'Loki did not do so well. But you have two more chances. What can Thialfi do?'

'I will run a race against anyone you choose,' said Thialfi.

So the king led the way to the great courtyard where the race would be held. Then he turned and looked down at the gods. Red sparks of anger flew from Thor's beard. He whispered to Thialfi that he must run as he had never run before.

The king chose a young giant named Hugi to race against Thialfi. At the signal, the two sprinted from the starting-line. But Hugi was so fast that he doubled back on the course and met Thialfi just a little way from the starting-point.

Thialfi tried twice more to outrun the giant, but both times the same thing happened. Thialfi hung his head in shame and returned to Thor's side.

Now Utgard-Loki turned to Thor and said, 'You gods are not our equals at all. It is up to you to prove me wrong – that is, if you still want to try! What contest will you engage in, to prove your godly strength?'

'A drinking match with anyone in the hall!' roared Thor.

'Softly,' said the giant. 'Your roaring tickles my ears.' And he motioned to his cupbearer to bring Thor a large drinking horn filled with wine.

Then the giant said to the god, 'A good drinker can empty the horn in one drink. Most of my subjects can do it in two, and even the weakest among them can do it in three.'

The horn did not look too large, although it was very long. Thor raised it to his lips confidently and gave a long, hard pull on the wine. But when he lowered the horn it was as full as when he raised it.

Angrily he drank again, but the wine remained at the same level in the horn. He tried a third time, harder than he had ever tried before. The wine sank in the horn only a little.

Utgard-Loki smiled. 'Indeed,' he said, 'we have judged the gods too high. You are not as strong as we thought. But we have a game which is only for children. Perhaps you would like to try it. See if you can lift my cat from the floor.'

Now, for the first time, Thor saw a big grey cat arching its back against the giant's foot. He put his hands under its belly and strained to lift it. The animal held its ground.

Thor tightened his belt of strength to the last notch, but he succeeded in raising only one foot of the grey cat.

'You are too little for my cat,' said the giant.

Thor's beard was fiery with sparks as he shouted, 'Little as you call me, let someone wrestle with me and I shall show you my strength!'

'I'm afraid you would have no chance with anyone here,' sighed the giant patiently, 'but my old nurse Elli might be willing to match her strength with yours.'

Dumbfounded, Thor saw a toothless old woman come into the hall. Before he could protest, she wound her arms around him and the harder he tried to break her hold, the firmer she stood. Finally he lost his balance and down he went.

'An end to these foolish contests!' said Utgard-Loki. 'Let us sit together at the banqueting table.'

Unhappy and ashamed, Thor and his companions feasted with the giants through the night. They made plans to start for home the next morning.

As the three gods made their farewells to the giants, Thor said, 'I have brought shame on all the gods! You must think us weak and stupid.'

'Far from it, thunder god,' said Utgard-Loki. 'I have tricked you from the first. I was the giant in the forest and that first night I tied up my knapsack with iron wire so that you could not break it. When you aimed three blows of your hammer at my head, I dodged. If I had not, that first one would have finished me. The blows landed on a mountain, where you will find three valleys, one very deep.

'In the first contest Loki ate his meal like hunger itself, but his opponent, Logi, was really wildfire. Hugi, who raced against Thialfi, was Thought, and who can keep up with thought? The horn you drank from reached to the sea. If you

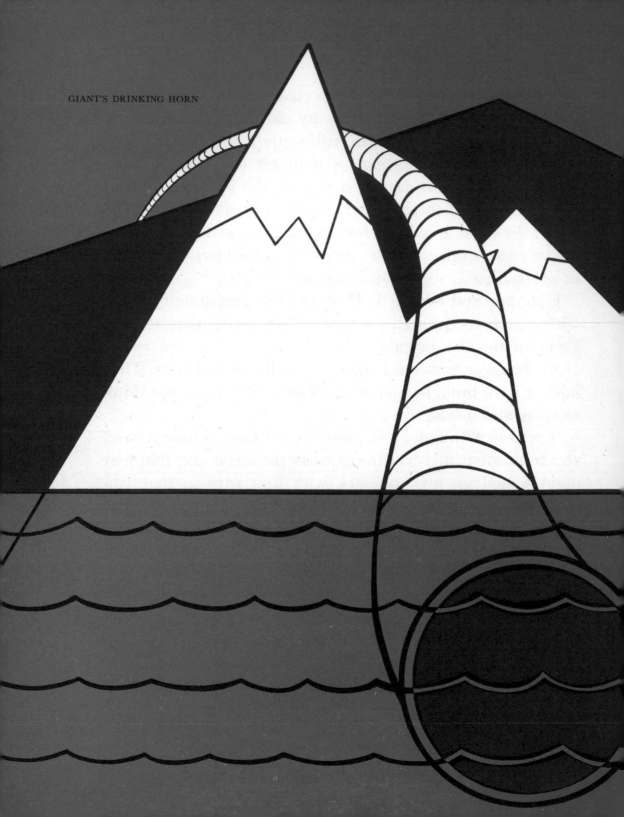

GIANT'S DRINKING HORN

look, you will be astonished to see how low the sea is this morning.'

'You have tricked us with magic!' bellowed Thor. 'What about your cat?'

'The cat was really the Midgard Serpent which encircles the world. You stretched him badly out of shape. He was barely able to bring his head and his tail together again. Elli, the nurse, was Old Age. No one in heaven or earth can stand up against her.'

'Now it is my turn for victory!' roared the infuriated thunder god and he raised his hammer to strike down the king of the giants. But before his eyes the giant dissolved in mist, leaving behind only his mocking laughter. Thor whirled to destroy the city, but it too had vanished, leaving the gods standing on an empty plain.

# LOKI AND THE GOLDEN APPLES

One day Odin and his brothers Hoenir and Loki were travelling through a barren part of Midgard, where man lived. Most of the time the gods flew over the earth in their chariots, but on this day they had decided to travel on foot, as men did. By sunset they were tired and hungry.

For their dinner they killed an ox which they found grazing near by. They put it in a cooking pot over a roaring fire. After a time, Loki lifted the lid of the pot to see if the ox was done.

'Raw!' he exclaimed. 'How could it take such a long time to cook?'

'Be patient, Loki,' said Odin, who never ate anything anyway and so could afford to be very patient.

Loki tried to be patient. But the smell of the boiling ox was so pleasant that finally he could not resist peeping at it again. Then he poked it with a stick and said in disgust, 'Still raw! I am so hungry! I'll put more wood on the fire so that it will burn hotter.'

Several hours passed and Odin himself got up to test the meat. The water was bubbling wildly in the pot and a delicious smell arose. But the meat was still raw.

'This is indeed strange!' said Odin. 'Someone has put a magic spell on our dinner.'

'Indeed! Indeed!' screeched a voice from high in the oak tree above them.

The gods looked up, startled, and saw a huge eagle perched in the topmost bough of the tree.

'If you will give me part of your meal, the meat shall be done and ready to eat in a second,' said the eagle.

Hoenir and Loki were so hungry that they shouted, 'Yes!'

As Loki lifted the lid from the pot, the giant bird swooped down. With his long, curved claws he snatched half the ox from the boiling water and bore it swiftly up to his perch on the tree-top. With a gulp and a terrible writhing of his long neck he swallowed the meat and swooped down again to grab the second half.

In a rage Loki grabbed a burning brand from the fire and struck at the bird as it flew by him. The brand stuck to the eagle's back like a magnet and the flame died as though it had been dashed in water. But Loki could not loosen his hand from the other end. The bird flew off, close to the ground, dragging the howling Loki over brush and stone.

'Don't worry about Loki,' said Odin to the frightened Hoenir. 'He is clever enough to break this spell. Let us find another ox for your dinner.'

The next day, a bruised and battered Loki returned to join Hoenir and Odin.

'How did you get away?' they asked him.

'It was simple,' said Loki. 'The creature got tired.'

45

Odin thought it strange that the eagle, which he knew to be a giant in disguise, should have let the god go without demanding a ransom. He was right. The giant had demanded a ransom and Loki had promised him the gentle Idun, goddess of youth, and also her golden apples, in return for his freedom.

When the gods returned to Asgard next day, Loki told the goddess of a tree in the forest which bore magic gold and silver fruit.

'Nonsense, Loki,' said Idun. 'You are joking as usual. But here, eat your apple before your whiskers turn white.'

Loki ate a golden apple and immediately felt rested and strong. All his bruises and hurts were gone. These are indeed wonderful, he thought to himself, and wondered how it would be when Idun and her apples were gone from Asgard. Still, he had made a bargain and the giant would no doubt give him a worse punishment if he did not fulfil it.

'Idun,' he said craftily, 'we have to eat your apples every day in order to renew our youth. But just one of the apples from the forest tree will give eternal youth. Come into the forest with me and you shall see.'

'It cannot be true,' said Idun. 'There are no apples in the world more marvellous than mine. Still, I should like to see the tree. I will go with you, but we must go without anyone's knowing. I am not supposed to leave the walls of Asgard.'

Loki smiled. Secrecy was just what he wanted. He guided Idun into the forest just as the sun was setting. Soon the

EAGLE THAT CARRIED LOKI AWAY

world was dark, for there was an oddly shaped cloud covering the moon.

Then Loki scrambled to the top of a small hill and called out into the darkness:

'Eagle! Eagle! I have brought Idun to you. Release me from your spell!'

The terrified Idun then saw that what had looked like a cloud was really the eagle's huge wings over the moon. As the bird swooped towards her, she saw its frightening claws and cruel red eyes. She screamed to Loki as the claws grabbed her and the monster bore her swiftly away.

When the gods came to Idun's garden the next day to eat their magic apples, they thought that she had gone visiting and were not worried. But a week passed and she did not return. Odin's hair grew thin. Thor's red beard was shot with grey. Freya veiled her face to hide her fading beauty.

Then one god remembered seeing Idun steal from her garden with Loki. He told Odin of this, and Odin summoned the mischief-maker and questioned him sternly.

At last Loki admitted what he had done.

'But what else could I do?' he asked. 'You left me to get out of trouble as best I could, so I bargained with the giant.'

'You must find a way to bring back Idun,' said Odin, 'or give your life in return. You paid too high a price for your wretched freedom.'

Loki borrowed the feathered cloak of Freya and changed

himself into a falcon. He flew to the rocky walls which surrounded the land of the giants and climbed to the top of them
to find the window of Idun's prison.

When Loki at last reached the sill of Idun's window, he
tumbled into the prison exhausted. There sat Idun weeping
pitifully.

'Poor little bird!' she exclaimed through her sobs. 'Where
have you come from?'

'From Asgard,' whispered Loki. 'Trust me and I will take
you back there.'

Then Loki touched the goddess and immediately she and
her basket of apples shrank to the size of a thumbnail. Loki
put them both in a walnut shell and flew away with it
clutched in his claws.

When they were about halfway home, Loki looked back
and saw a black speck on the horizon. The eagle had discovered that Idun was gone! Loki flew faster and faster, but
the eagle came closer and closer. As Loki neared the walls of
Asgard he felt the fiery breath of the eagle only a few yards
behind him.

When the gods saw Loki flying desperately and the eagle
about to overtake him, Odin cried out, 'Build fires on the
walls! The giant shall not escape, even if that wicked Loki
does not reach safety!'

Just as the eagle reached out to grab him with its strong
beak, Loki flew over the walls and dropped to the ground

THE RESCUE OF IDUN

with his precious load. The gods quickly lit the fires and caught the eagle before it could turn back. The bird's wings flamed and it fell to the ground. Immediately it took its real form of a mountain giant with beard singed by the flames. As the giant scrambled to his feet, he faced the thunder god Thor. That was the last thing he ever saw.

There was a feast of celebration in Asgard that night; and the merriest guest was Loki, boasting about his rescue of Idun just as though the whole trouble had not been of his making in the first place.

# THE BIGGEST KETTLE IN THE WORLD

The god of the sea, Aegir, invited the gods of Asgard to celebrate the feast of the harvest with him.

'I am sure I can please your appetites, but my brewing kettle is much too small to hold all the ale you will drink at my feast. I shall need one at least a mile deep and a mile wide.'

Such a kettle had never been seen, but Thor knew that if one existed, Hymir the frost giant would certainly have it. He said to the god of the sea, 'You shall have your kettle for the feast, old man. Tyr and I will go in search of it.'

The two gods rumbled across the sky in Thor's goat-drawn chariot to Hymir's ice palace in Jotunheim. There the hoofs of the shaggy goats clattered across the icy courtyard and threw up sprays of chipped ice as they were reined to a stop in front of the palace door.

Hymir's wife greeted them with a warning, 'You are welcome, gods! But my husband is returning home soon and you must hide for your own safety. Sometimes he is very short-tempered and will kill a guest with a single glance!'

'What! Thor, god of thunder, hide from a frost giant?' Thor protested. But Tyr reminded him that they had come to get the kettle and should do as they were told. No sooner had the two gods hidden themselves under two large cooking pots than the giant stalked into the room. Snow flew from his hair and the icicles clinging to his beard made strange music as they jangled together. Suddenly he stopped.

'Woman!' he roared 'There is someone hidden here!'

With that he flashed a lightning glance at the two pots where the gods were hidden. The pots flew into a thousand pieces. Furiously the giant rushed towards Thor and Tyr, but his wife stopped him.

'They are friendly, Hymir. Let them stay and be welcome.'

'Oh, very well. But now I shall have to go and kill some oxen to feed them,' he growled.

When they all sat down for dinner, the table groaned beneath three huge oxen. Curious to see in what great pot such beasts had been cooked, Thor glanced secretly about the room. His eyes fell on the largest kettle he had ever seen. It was surely a full mile wide and deep, and just the one for the sea god's feast. But he decided to wait to ask about it until the next day, when the giant might be in a better mood.

It was a good thing he did, for presently he made the giant still angrier by eating two of the oxen himself. When the giant saw the great pile of well-gnawed bones on Thor's plate, he left the table and stalked up and down the room, muttering, 'Now I shall have to get up early in the morning to go fishing and get more food for those ravenous gods' appetites!'

53

Thinking to soften the giant's temper, Thor went down to the ocean early the next morning to help Hymir with his fishing.

'Good morning, Hymir,' he said, and proceeded to kill the giant's largest ox for bait, which did nothing to make the giant feel any better. Thor loaded his bait on to the boat and the god and the giant rowed out to sea.

When they came to the giant's usual place for fishing, Hymir said, 'We have come far enough! If we go any further we will come to where the head of the terrible Midgard Serpent lies.'

'Afraid, Hymir?' asked Thor. 'I should like to go a little farther.'

Thor rowed on and on until they came to the spot where he thought the serpent's head would be. He began angling for the monster while the giant was baiting his line. There was good fishing that morning. Hymir caught two whales, which he thought would be enough for breakfast!

He shouted to Thor to pull in his line and row back, but the thunder god felt a sudden jerk on the line.

'Not now, giant!' he shouted. 'I have hooked the Midgard Serpent!' The frost giant looked frightened enough to melt. He clutched the sides of the boat and closed his eyes tightly as the thunder god braced himself for the struggle with the serpent.

The sea was churned into mile-high black waves as the

monster fought and twisted to get away from Thor's hook. The boat leaped and fell crazily with the mountains of water. One minute it rose higher than the icebergs, the next it fell almost to the bottom of the sea.

Suddenly the ugly head of the monster rose out of the water at the side of the boat. Shouting, Thor raised his hammer to deal the death blow to the Midgard Serpent. But Hymir, fearful that the boat would sink and that they would both be eaten by the monster, cut Thor's line and the serpent, hissing, sank under the wild water.

Furious at being cheated of his prey, Thor now raised his hammer to strike the giant. The terrified Hymir bellowed, 'No! No! I will give you anything you ask, but spare me!'

'You made me lose my catch, Hymir! I should have your icy head for that! But I will be generous. Let us return home and we will talk about it.'

They rowed back without a word. After beaching the boat, Hymir heaved the two whales over his shoulder and Thor, in his turn, carried the boat, oars and fishing tackle.

After breakfasting on the whales, Hymir felt less frightened and not so willing to give Thor what he might ask. However, he asked the thunder god what reward he demanded. Thor replied, 'Your biggest kettle: the one hanging over there.'

'Then you must prove to me that you are strong enough to be worthy of such a kettle. If you can break my drinking cup, the kettle is yours.'

THOR CARRIES HOME THE GIANT KETTLE

Thor was angry with Hymir for breaking his word, but as he wanted the kettle very badly, he said nothing.

Thor threw the cup with all his might against the stone hearth. It did not break. Again and again he threw it without making the slightest dent in it. Then Hymir's wife whispered to him that the only thing harder than the cup was the giant's skull. Thor hurled it at the giant's forehead, and the cup broke into a hundred pieces and fell to the floor.

'The kettle is yours, Thor. But now try to carry it with you,' jeered Hymir.

Thor tried twice, but could not budge it from the floor. He tightened his belt of strength and braced himself and pulled again and again.

The kettle rose at last. But so firmly had Thor braced himself on his sturdy legs that as the kettle rose, Thor's feet went through the floor, the kettle flew up and the ceiling came crashing down. Quickly, before the giant could recover from his surprise, Thor seized the kettle, balanced it on his head, and so set forth with it for the sea god's palace and the harvest feast.

# FREYA'S NECKLACE

One night the keen ears of Heimdall, watchman of the Rainbow Bridge, caught the sound of soft footsteps near Freya's palace. He peered through the darkness and now saw Loki entering Freya's window disguised as a fly.

Heimdall immediately guessed that Loki was going to steal Freya's necklace while she slept. This necklace, of purest gold, was the symbol of the fruitfulness of the earth. If it were stolen from the goddessess's neck, all the growing plants on earth would perish. Heimdall knew that he must stop Loki from doing this terrible thing.

Meanwhile the mischief-maker stood by the sleeping Freya's bed, trying to work out how to steal the necklace without waking her. She was sleeping on her back, the clasp of the necklace hidden beneath her golden hair.

Suddenly Loki had an idea. He muttered softly to himself, and immediately his magic words changed him into a flea! He crept under the sheet and bit Freya's side. Freya scratched and turned over. The clasp of the necklace was in full sight of the thieving god.

Gently Loki opened the clasp. The necklace fell glittering on the goddess's silken pillow. He seized the golden strand and fled.

But as Loki raced across the moonlit courtyard, he was suddenly confronted by Heimdall with his shining sword. The sword flashed down in a mighty arc to cut off Loki's head.

Loki's mocking laughter rang out. Before the sword could strike, the mischief-maker had changed himself into a flickering blue flame.

'You shall not escape so easily!' roared Heimdall and changed himself into a rain cloud from which torrents of rain deluged on to the flame.

But just as the flame was about to splutter out, there arose from it a great polar bear.

'Hah! I shall swallow the raindrops, you golden-toothed rain cloud!' roared Loki's voice from the bear's mouth.

Immediately Heimdall changed himself into a bear, growling furiously. The two bears fought and roared and clawed each other. Heimdall was the strongest, and in a little while Loki knew that he was beaten. He quickly changed himself into a seal and slipped out of Heimdall's clutches.

Just as quickly, Heimdall too changed into a seal and hit Loki about with his shining black flippers. This time Loki did not escape. Sullenly he handed over the necklace to the watchman of the Rainbow Bridge. But as he stumbled back to Asgard, sore and beaten, he shouted over his shoulder, 'Another time, Golden-Tooth!'

Heimdall knew that there was no end to Loki's trickery.

# THE DEATH OF BALDUR

Baldur the beautiful, god of light and spring, was troubled by terrible dreams. Every night the dream was the same—his life was in danger. Someone wanted to take it away. Then light and spring would no longer work their wondrous magic in the world. His face grew sad, and all Asgard wept to see the best-loved god of all so changed.

At last Baldur went to see his mother, the goddess Frigga, and asked her for her help.

'Do not worry,' said Frigga. 'I shall journey over the world and seek the help of everything on earth. Then you will be safe.'

So Frigga went to see fire and water, stones and trees, and all metals. She talked to diseases and poisons, birds and beasts and creeping things. She made them all promise not to hurt her son. When she went back to Asgard, she hurried to Baldur and told him, 'You are safe from harm. Don't be afraid any more.'

From then on the gods amused themselves by throwing stones at Baldur, hurling daggers at him and even swords and battle-axes. They all fell without harming him.

After a while, the gods made a sort of game out of throwing

HODUR THROWS THE MISTLETOE DART

things at Baldur and seeing them fall without touching him. They hoped it would make him forget his bad dreams.

One day Loki, who had not joined in the sport, watched the gods hurling their weapons at Baldur. He had always envied the goodness and beauty that made the god such a favourite, and now his envy became ungovernable.

'I must find a way to hurt him!' he whispered to himself and assuming the disguise of an old gossip, he went to call on the goddess Frigga.

'Is it true,' he whined in his old woman's voice, 'that everything on earth has promised not to hurt Baldur?'

'Everything!' said the goddess.

'Are you sure?' asked Loki craftily. 'You forgot not one small pebble, not one tiny leaf?'

'I forgot nothing,' said Frigga. 'But there was one small shrub called mistletoe which I did not ask because it is so little.'

The delighted Loki left the goddess and, after changing back to his natural form, went to the place where the mistletoe grew and cut off a twig. He whittled the twig into a sharp-pointed dart. Then he went to the great hall where the gods were amusing themselves by throwing weapons at Baldur. He immediately sought out the blind god Hodur and asked, 'Would you like to throw something at Baldur, too?'

'I have nothing to throw and I could not see to throw it if I had,' said Hodur.

'That is no problem, my friend,' said Loki. 'Here is a little dart. Take it in your hand and I will guide your aim.'

Smiling, the god took the mistletoe. Loki guided his hand. The dart flew straight and true to Baldur's heart. The god fell dead.

When Frigga learned of her son's death, she said through her tears, 'Whoever wants my love and goodwill must ride to Hel and ask Hela, goddess of the dead, to give Baldur back to us.'

Hermod, son of Odin, volunteered to go. For nine days and nine nights he rode his father's great horse Sleipnir through dark and mysterious valleys, until he came to the golden bridge which crossed the river Gyroll into Hel. The maiden who guarded the gate recognized the great horse of Odin and allowed its rider to pass.

Hermod rode immediately to the coal-black palace of Hela. Inside he saw Baldur feasting at a long banqueting table. Hermod recognized Hela at the head of the table and asked that Baldur be allowed to return to Asgard with him.

Hela, her blue face terrible with triumph, answered, 'Go back to earth and ask every living thing to weep for him. If there is even one among the living who will not weep, Baldur must remain with me.'

Now the gods sent messengers to the farthest corners of the world, asking all things to weep for the death of Baldur. Every man, animal and plant wept for the god. The very rocks shed tears. The messengers were about to return in triumph with the news that Baldur would live again when they came upon an old hag in a dark cave.

'Weep, mother,' they commanded her, 'for Baldur, the god of light and spring is dead!'

The hag cackled evilly. 'Who loves light and spring?' she shrilled. 'Not I!'

And so it was that Baldur's soul never returned to Asgard. Odin commanded that huge pines be brought down from the mountain for Baldur's funeral pyre. The gods built the great bonfire on the deck of Baldur's mighty ship Ringhorn. They decorated the ship with garlands of flowers and weighted down the decks with costly gifts.

For hours the gods passed by the couch on which Baldur lay dead. At last Nanna, his wife, drew near. Her grief was so great that her heart broke and she was placed beside Baldur to make the final voyage.

As the funeral ship drifted out to sea, the fire kindled on its deck by Thor's hammer set the sky aglow. The gods returned sadly to Asgard as the final spark of light disappeared beneath the sea. The world was in darkest mourning for Baldur the beautiful and good.

THOR TRAPS LOKI

# LOKI'S PUNISHMENT

At last the gods knew that Loki was not only a mischief-maker but a god so wicked that he must no longer be allowed to roam the world freely. Baldur's death had convinced them of that. And so they held council, sitting on their golden thrones, debating what they should do to restrain this evil before it was too late and man and gods perished in the dark.

Loki heard their voices raised in stern debate. Terrified, he fled from Asgard and found refuge in the mountains. There he built a house with a door on each side, so that if the gods approached one door he could escape out of the other.

The gods finally discovered Loki's hiding-place. But they did not approach by either door. They surrounded the house, and Loki was trapped. Desperately he scurried from room to room, looking for a place to hide. At last he changed himself into a salmon and dived from the window into the brook that ran by the house. There he hid quivering beneath the rocks that overhung the deepest pool. Loki did not see Thor pick up the fishing net that he himself had invented in his long hours alone. He only heard Thor roar, 'Loki, your time has come! You cannot escape by any of your tricks!'

Softly Thor dropped the net over the water. Loki, seeing

its shadow and not recognizing it as his net, swam out to see what the shadow was. The net swooped down and trapped him. Loki thrashed wildly in the net, trying to escape, but Thor grabbed him by the tail. He grabbed so hard that he flattened the fish's tail, which is the reason why all salmon have thin tails today.

When Loki finally assumed his real form once more, the gods chained him to a mountain cliff. There he is today. When he grows restless and tries to break his chain, the earth trembles and men cry, 'Earthquake!' and hide until he is quiet again.

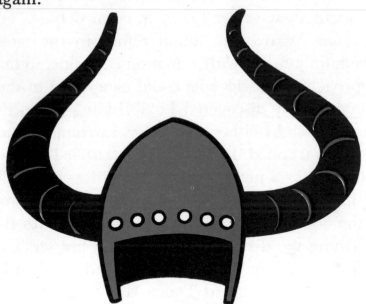

# INDEX

HUGIN